PIPSQUEA

MAZE DAY

Written and Illustrated by
Patrick Merrell

SCHOLASTIC INC.

New York   Toronto   London   Auckland   Sydney

Dedicated to
June and
Charlie Merrell

ISBN 0-590-98523-X

Copyright © 1997 by Patrick Merrell. Book design by Patrick Merrell.
Pipsqueaks name, logo, and characters are a trademark of Patrick Merrell.
All rights reserved. Published by Scholastic Inc.

12 11 10 9 8 7 6 5 4 3 2 1   7 8 9/9 0 1 2/0

Printed in the U.S.A.   23
First Scholastic printing, May 1997

We're the Pipsqueaks, we love games,
but mazes most of all.
Once a year we hold a fair
with mazes large and small.

The day is known as Maze Day,
a day that makes us grin.
If you're ready, turn the page,
and let the fun begin....

Attention, maze solvers.
You can do all these mazes by
pointing with your finger.

Line Up

Maze Day! Maze Day!
Here at last.
A day of mazes,
what a blast!

To the entrance.
There's the sign!
Hurry up
and stand in line.

There are always lots of lines for Maze Day.
Can you figure out which line leads to the big "Entrance" sign?
Which line would you get on to buy a piece of cheese?

Crazy Crossroads

Cars and buses,
trucks and trams.
Pipsqueaks caught
in traffic jams.

Some drive up,
and some drive down,
trying to get
through this town.

Can you find the route along this roadway that will
take us from one traffic cone to the other?

The Puddle Path

We are planning
in a huddle,
how to get
across this puddle.

We're not sure
which way is best—
which way across
this tricky test.

Can you find the one path of sticks that
will help us get across the puddle?
Which path will take us to the frog?

Vine
Time

It's easy climbing
up in trees.
But getting down
is not a breeze.

Lots of branches,
many vines.
It sure would help
if there were signs.

By walking on branches and climbing down vines, can
you find a way for us to get down to the ground?
(To get to a lower branch, a vine must reach all the way to it.)
How many different animals can you find in this maze?

High Flyers

The next event
that we are holding
calls for lots
of paper folding.

Paper planes
are what we're making.
Flying trips
are what we're taking.

Can you follow all four of the Pipsqueaks'
paths to see where they end up?

The Boat Float

Here's a maze
that we have planned.
A maze of water
in the sand.

Hop aboard
a raft that floats.
Join us, won't you,
in our boats.

Can you find the watery path
that leads to our sand castle?

START

Mayo

Cola

FINISH

Pipsqueaks on Parade

Watch the Pipsqueaks
march through town.
Hiking up,
and hopping down.

Some skip left,
and some scoot right.
Some skedaddle
out of sight.

Starting below, can you follow the line of
parading Pipsqueaks all the way to the big drum?

END!

Lunch Lines

Chunks of cheese
are piled up.
Grab your fork,
a knife and cup.

Is there one
you'd like to munch?
Pick a string
and find your lunch.

It's lunchtime!
Can you follow each piece of yarn to
see which pile of cheese it leads to?

Squeeze
Play

Squeeze the mustard.
Squeeze the ketchup.
Squeeze too slow,
and you must catch up.

Splat and splatter,
spurt and spray.
Squirt and squish
and squeeze away.

What a mess! Can you follow both of the
Pipsqueaks from where they started squeezing their
ketchup and mustard bottles to where they ended up?

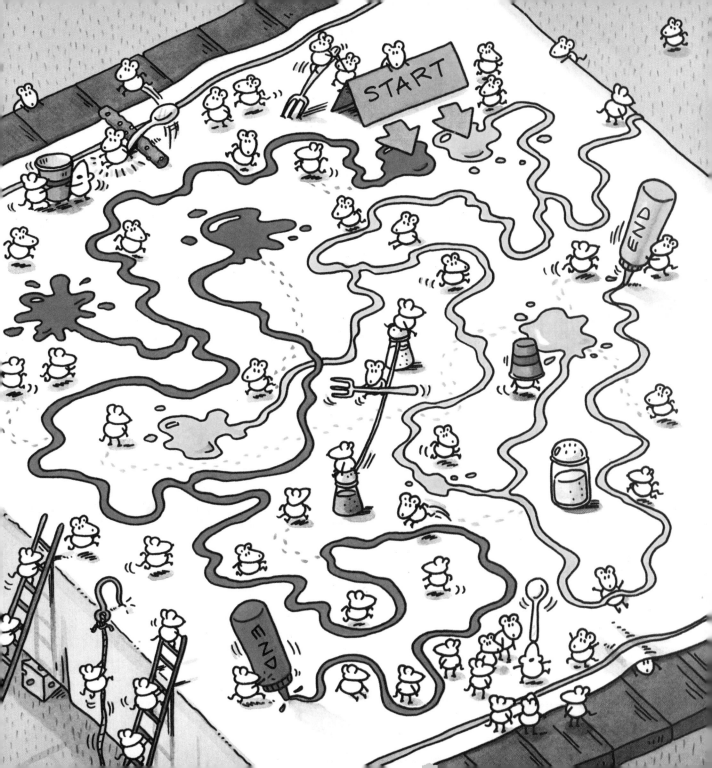

Tub to Sub

In the bathtub
we are brimming.
In the water
we are swimming.

Underwater
there's a sub.
Can you get there?
Glub, glub, glub.

We've gone underwater.
By following the rope, can you find a way from tub to sub?

Map Makers

We each have
a different marker.
Some draw lighter,
some draw darker.

We've drawn a map
that's red and blue.
Yellow, orange,
and purple, too.

We've drawn five roads on our map.
Beginning at "Start," can you follow each
path to the Pipsqueak who has drawn it?

The Hole Stroll

Pick a shovel,
grab a pick.
Pick a spot
and dig in quick!

Search and scour,
Hunt and measure.
Dig down deep
for buried treasure.

Jewels! Coins! Cheese!
Which Pipsqueaks' path leads to the treasure?

Sleepy Heads

Maze Day sure was
lots of fun.
But time's run out,
and now we're done.

Before you leave,
just one last test—
we need to find
a place to rest.

Thanks for helping us with Maze Day.
Can you help us find the way to our beds?

START

THE
END

Grubby

Deke

Squeaky

Nosey

Cheesy

Nashville

Scr...

How to Have Your Own MAZE DAY

**You can celebrate Maze Day, too.
There are probably lots of things in your
home you could use to make mazes....**

One of the best ways to
make mazes is to draw them.
You can use paper. Or a
chalkboard. Or paint a maze
using different colors.

Do you have some blocks?
Blocks are great for making mazes.
Make roads using the blocks,
or paths using the blocks as walls.

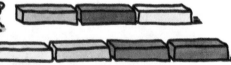

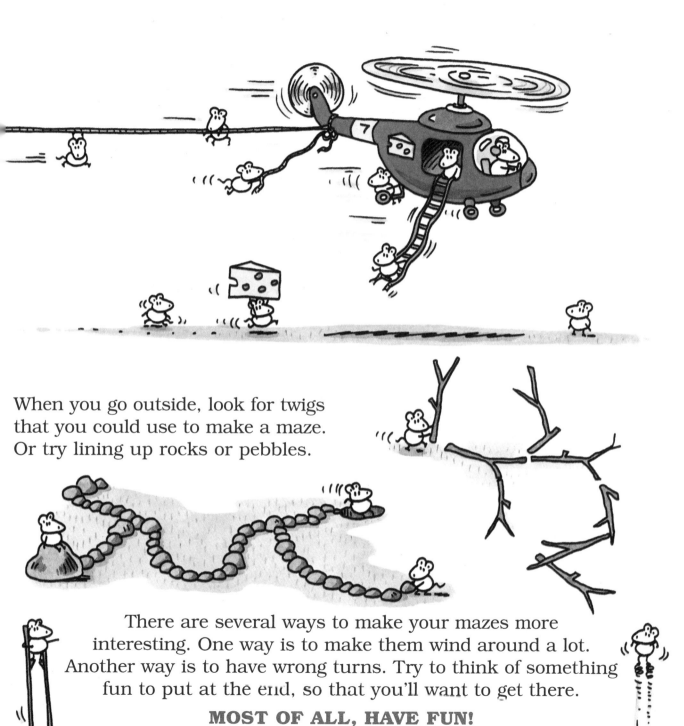

When you go outside, look for twigs
that you could use to make a maze.
Or try lining up rocks or pebbles.

There are several ways to make your mazes more
interesting. One way is to make them wind around a lot.
Another way is to have wrong turns. Try to think of something
fun to put at the end, so that you'll want to get there.

MOST OF ALL, HAVE FUN!

Cheese Chase

Go back now,
look closely please.
In each maze
you'll find a cheese.

When you see it,
do not freeze.
Speak right up
and holler, "Cheese!"

There is at least one piece of cheese in each maze.
Can you find them all?